Arranged for *all* electronic keyboards *by Kenneth Baker.*

THE COMPLETE KEYBOARD PLAYER

Chart Hits

£8.25

This publication is not authorised for sale in
the United States of America and/or Canada

Wise Publications
London/New York/Paris/Sydney/Copenhagen/Madrid/Tokyo

Exclusive Distributors:
Music Sales Limited
8/9 Frith Street, London W1D 3JB, England.
Music Sales Pty Limited
120 Rothschild Avenue, Rosebery, NSW 2018, Australia.

This book © Copyright 2000 by
Wise Publications.
Order No. AM962951
ISBN 0-7119-8055-1

Unauthorised reproduction of any part of this publication by any
means including photocopying is an infringement of copyright.

Compiled by Nick Crispin.
Music arranged by Kenneth Baker.
Music processed by Dakota Music Service.
Cover photograph (All Saints) courtesy of LFI.
Printed in the United Kingdom by
Printwise (Haverhill) Limited, Haverhill, Suffolk.

Your Guarantee of Quality
As publishers, we strive to produce every book
to the highest commercial standards.
The music has been freshly engraved and the book has been
carefully designed to minimise awkward page turns and to make
playing from it a real pleasure.
Particular care has been given to specifying acid-free, neutral-sized paper
made from pulps which have not been elemental chlorine bleached.
This pulp is from farmed sustainable forests and was produced with special
regard for the environment. Throughout, the printing and binding have been
planned to ensure a sturdy, attractive publication which should give years of enjoyment.
If your copy fails to meet our high standards, please inform us and
we will gladly replace it.

Music Sales' complete catalogue describes thousands of titles and is available in
full colour sections by subject, direct from Music Sales Limited.
Please state your areas of interest and send a cheque/postal order for £1.50 for postage to:
Music Sales Limited, Newmarket Road, Bury St. Edmunds, Suffolk IP33 3YB.

www.musicsales.com

YELLOW

Words & Music by Guy Berryman, Jon Buckland, Will Champion & Chris Martin

© Copyright 2000 BMG Music Publishing Limited, Bedford House, 69-79 Fulham High Street, London SW6.
This arrangement © Copyright 2000 BMG Music Publishing Limited.
All Rights Reserved. International Copyright Secured.

Voice: oboe
Rhythm: 8 beat
Tempo: slow (♩=86)

VERSES

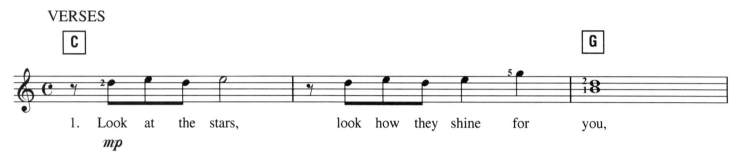

1. Look at the stars, look how they shine for you,

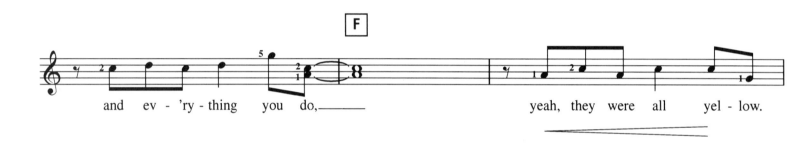

and ev - 'ry - thing you do,___ yeah, they were all yel - low.

2. I came a - long, I wrote a song for you,
3. I swam a - cross, I jumped a - cross for you,

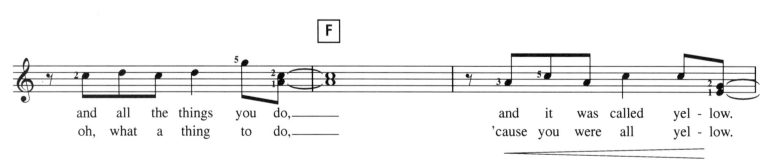

and all the things you do,___ and it was called yel - low.
oh, what a thing to do,___ 'cause you were all yel - low.

— I drew a line.
— I drew a line.___ So then I took my turn,
I drew a line for you,

4

NATURAL BLUES

Words by Vera Hall. Music by Vera Hall & Moby

'Natural Blues' is based on the song 'Trouble So Hard' (Words & Music by Vera Hall)

© Copyright 1960, 1999 Progressive Music Publishing Company/Carlin Music Corporation,
Iron Bridge House, 3 Bridge Approach, London NW1/The Little Idiot Music/
Warner Chappell Music Limited, Griffin House, 161 Hammersmith Road, London W6.
All Rights Reserved. International Copyright Secured.

Voice: folk guitar pad

Rhythm: rock

Tempo: medium (♩=108)

CHORUS

Oh Lor - dy, trou - ble so hard. Oh Lor - dy,

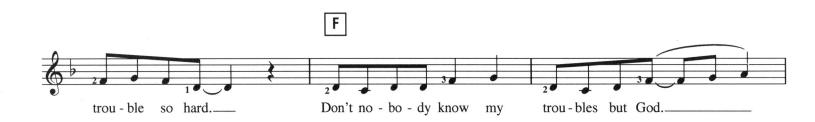

trou - ble so hard. Don't no - bo - dy know my trou - bles but God.

Don't no - bo - dy no my trou - bles but God. Oh Lor - dy,

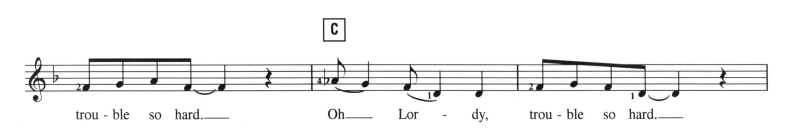

trou - ble so hard. Oh Lor - dy, trou - ble so hard.

Don't no - bo - dy know my trou - bles but God. Don't no - bo - dy no my

VERSE

(FINE)

1. **Dm**

trou - bles but God.____

(stop rhythm last time) *mp*

1. Went down the hill____ oth - er day.____ My

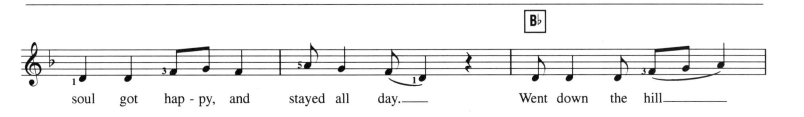

soul got hap - py, and stayed all day.____ Went down the hill____

B♭

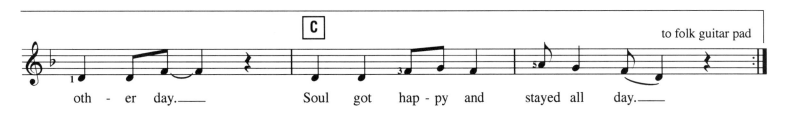

C

oth - er day.____ Soul got hap - py and stayed all day.____

to folk guitar pad

VERSE

2. **Dm**

2. Went in the room,____ did - n't stay long.____ Looked on the bed____ and

mp

B♭

bro - ther was dead. Went in the room,____ did - n't stay____ long.

C

D.C. al FINE
to folk guitar pad

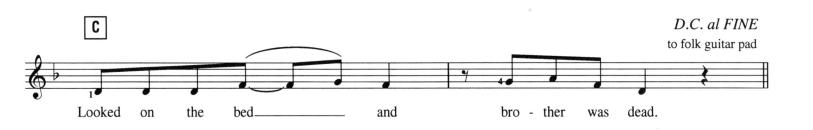

Looked on the bed____ and bro - ther was dead.

7

TAKE ON ME

Words & Music by Morten Harket, Mags Furuholmen & Pal Waaktaar

© Copyright 1984 ATV Music Limited.
Sony/ATV Music Publishing (UK) Limited, 10 Great Marlborough Street, London W1.
All Rights Reserved. International Copyright Secured.

Voice: piano pad
Rhythm: disco pop
Tempo: fast (♩=160)

BLACK COFFEE

Words & Music by Tom Nichols, Alexander Soos & Kirsty Elizabeth

© Copyright 2000 Good Groove Songs Limited/Universal Music Publishing Limited, 77 Fulham Palace Road, London W6.
All Rights Reserved. International Copyright Secured.

Voice: human voice
Rhythm: 8 beat
Tempo: medium (♩=120)

VERSES

1. Night swim-ming, beach walk-ing, al-ways si - lent, ne - ver talk-ing. Then you call my name,— and I
2. Day - dream-ing, chain-smo-king, al-ways laugh-ing, al-ways jo-king, I re-main the same,— did I

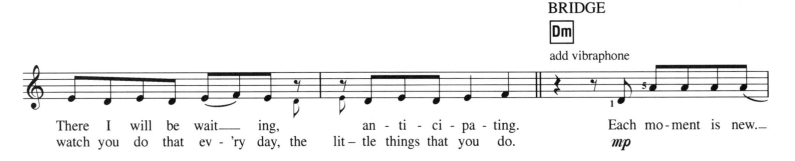

know in-side I love you. Sail a - way, I miss you more, un - til you see the shore.
tell you that I love you? Brush your teeth and pour a cup of black— cof-fee out, I love to

BRIDGE

add vibraphone

There I will be wait— ing, an - ti - ci - pa - ting. Each mo-ment is new.—
watch you do that ev - 'ry day, the lit — tle things that you do.

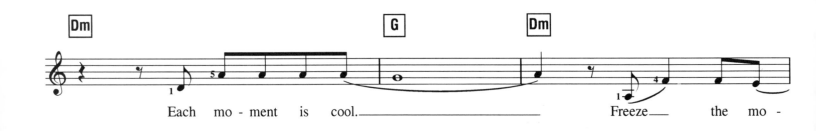

Freeze— the mo - ment.— Each mo - ment is cool.— Freeze— the mo -

SEASONS IN THE SUN

Words by Rod McKuen. Music by Jacques Brel

© Copyright 1961 Edward B. Marks Music Company, USA.
Carlin Music Corporation, Iron Bridge House, 3 Bridge Approach, London NW1
for the British Commonwealth (excluding Canada and Australasia) and the Republic of Ireland.
All Rights Reserved. International Copyright Secured.

Voice: accordion
Rhythm: 8 beat
Tempo: medium (♩=88)

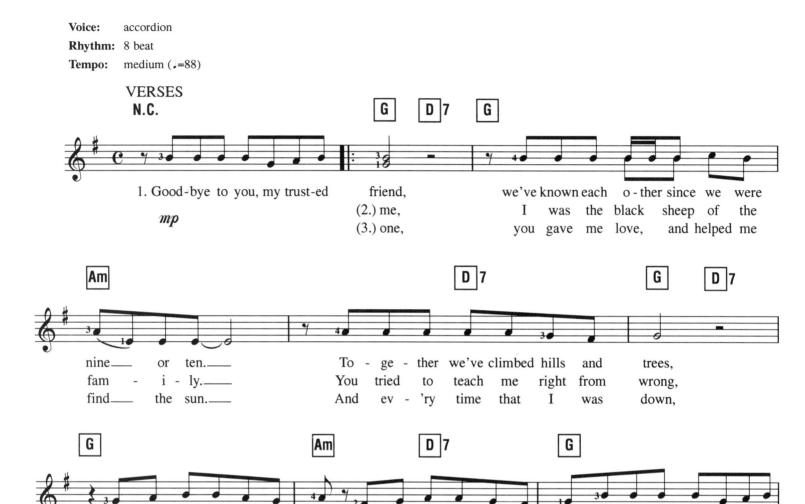

1. Good-bye to you, my trust-ed friend, we've known each o-ther since we were
(2.) me, I was the black sheep of the
(3.) one, you gave me love, and helped me

nine___ or ten.___ To-ge-ther we've climbed hills and trees,
fam-i-ly.___ You tried to teach me right from wrong,
find___ the sun.___ And ev-'ry time that I was down,

learned of love and A B C's, skinned our hearts, and skinned our knees. Good-bye my friend, it's hard to
too much wine, and too much song, won-der how I got a-long. Good-bye, Pa-pa, it's hard to
you would al-ways come a-round, get my feet back on the ground. Good-bye, Mich-elle, it's hard to

die,___ when all the birds are sing-ing in___ the sky.
die,___ when all the birds are sing-ing in___ the sky.
die,___ when all the birds are sing-ing in___ the sky.___

Now that Spring is in the air, pret-ty girls are ev-'ry-
Now that Spring is in the air, lit-tle chil-dren ev-'ry-
Now that Spring is in the air, with the flow-ers ev-'ry-

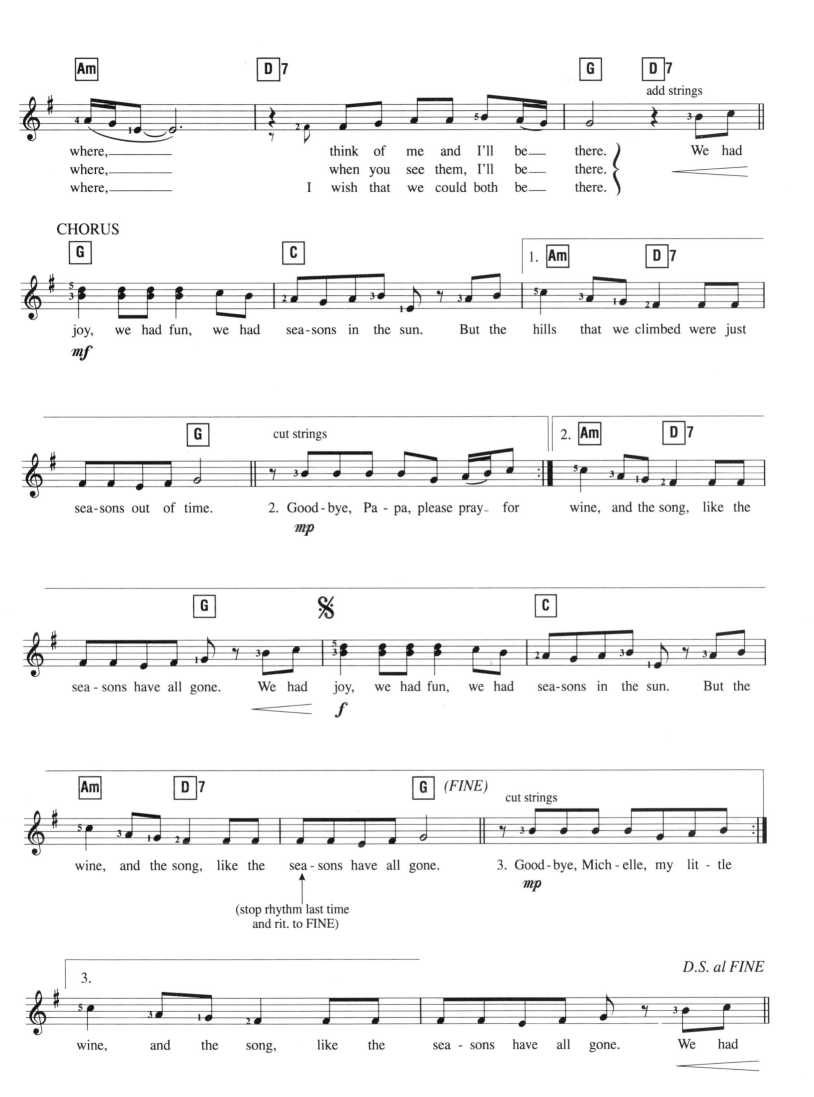

IT FEELS SO GOOD

Words & Music by Sonique, Linus Burdick & Simon Belofsky

© Copyright 1998 Linus Burdick Publishing/BMG Music Publishing Limited,
Bedford House, 69-79 Fulham High Street, London SW6 (50%)/
Universal Music Publishing Limited, 77 Fulham Palace Road, London W6 (40%)/
Peermusic (UK) Limited, 8-14 Verulam Street, London WC1 (10%).
All Rights Reserved. International Copyright Secured.

Voice: string ensemble
Rhythm: dance pop
Tempo: fairly fast (♩=136)

VERSES

1. You al - ways make me smile_____ when I'm feel - ing down.
2. (freely) Ooh,_____ I want you to un - der - stand how I feel,_____

You give me such a vibe,_____ it's to - tal - ly
yeah,_____

bo - na fide._____ Mm._____ It's not the way you walk.
deep in - side._____ Oh,_____

And it ain't the way you talk.
oh, you made me feel_____

It ain't the job you got_____ that keeps me sat - is - fied. (Your_
what I need to feel, yes,_____ in my heart._____

add guitar

CHORUS

love, it feels so good.) And that's what takes___ me___ high.___

(High - er than I've been be - fore.) Your

love___ it keeps___ me a - live.___ (Thought I should let you___

know.) That your touch it means___ so___ much.___

(When I'm a - lone at___ night.) It's___ you___ I'm al - ways think - in' of.___

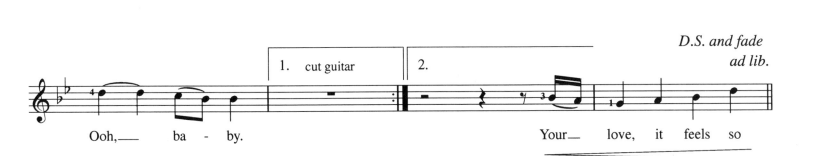

D.S. and fade ad lib.

1. cut guitar   2.

Ooh,___ ba - by.   Your___ love, it feels so

SING IT BACK

Words & Music by Mark Brydon & Roisin Murphy

© Copyright 1998 Chrysalis Music Limited,
The Chrysalis Building, Bramley Road, London W10.
All Rights Reserved. International Copyright Secured.

Voice: gut guitar
Rhythm: salsa
Tempo: medium (♩=124)

VERSES

1. When you are rea - dy___ I will___ sur - ren - der,___ take me___ and do as___ you
2. Can I con - trol this___ emp - ty___ de - lu - sion,___ lost in___ the fi - re be -
3. No, you can't help it___ if you have___ been temp - ted,___ by fruit hang - ing ripe on___ the

wish.   Have what you want, your___ way's al - ways___ the best way.___
low?   And you come run - ning,___ your eyes will___ be o - pen.
tree.   And I feel use - less, don't care what___ the truth is,___

(echo) -   I have suc - cumbed to___ this
(echo) -   And when you come back,___ I'll
you will be here, come the day.   Truth do you hear me,___ don't

pas - sive___ sen - sa - tion,___ peace - ful - ly fall - ing___ a - way.
be as___ you want me,___ on - ly___ so ea - ger___ to please.
try to___ come near me,___ so tir - ed,___ I sleep thro'___ the lie.

I am a zom - bie,___ your wish will___ com - mand me,___ laugh as I fall to my
My lit - tle song will___ keep you___ be - side me,___ think - ing your name as I
If you de - sire___ to lay here___ be - side me,___ come to my sweet me - lo -

mf

16

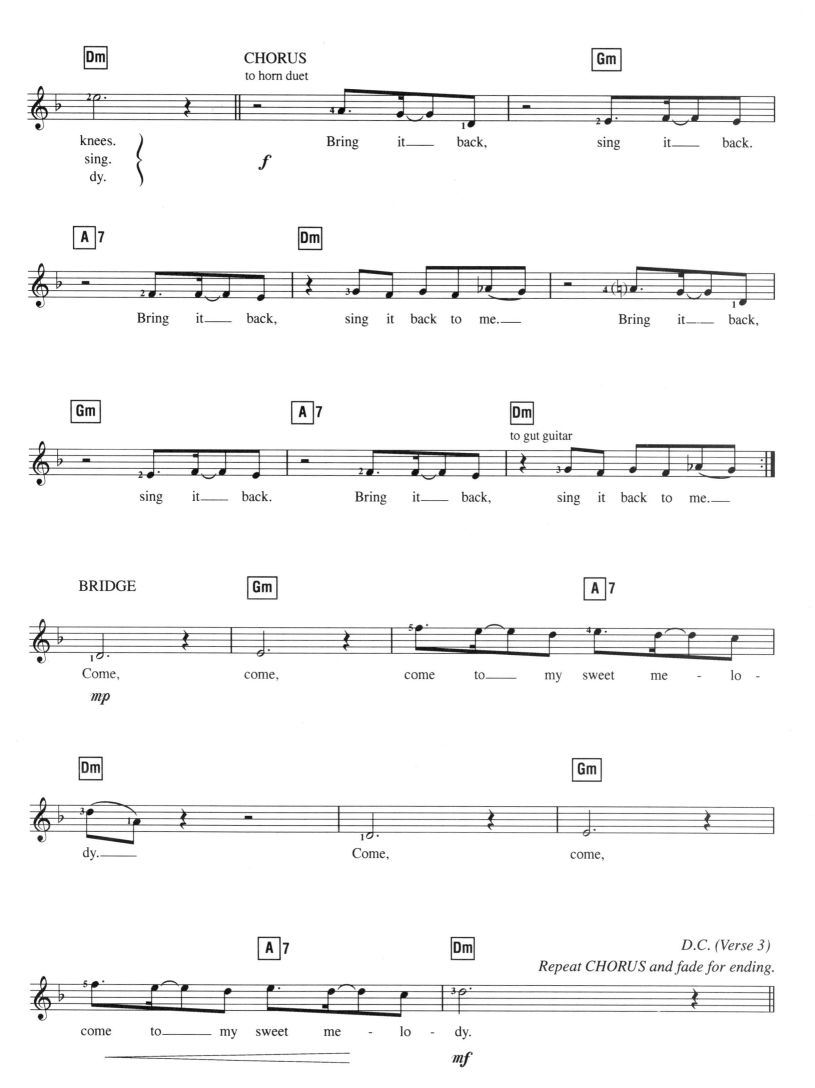

SUNDAY MORNING CALL

Words & Music by Noel Gallagher

© Copyright 2000 Oasis Music, Creation Songs Limited & Sony/
ATV Music Publishing (UK) Limited, 10 Great Marlborough Street, London W1.
All Rights Reserved. International Copyright Secured.

Voice: tenor saxophone
Rhythm: hard rock
Tempo: slow (♩.=80)

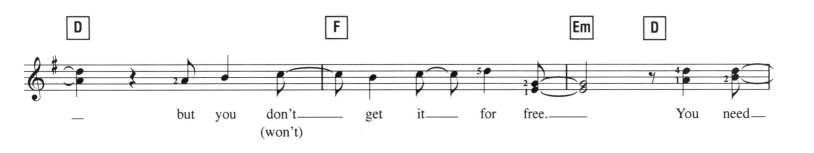

— but you don't___ get it___ for free.___ You need___
(won't)

— more time,___ coz your thoughts___ and words___ won't last___

___ for - e - ver more.___ And I'm not sure___ if it -'ll e -

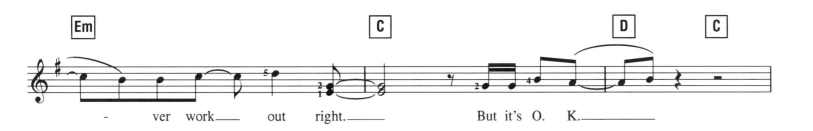

- ver work___ out right.___ But it's O. K.___

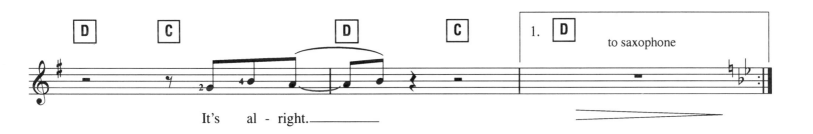

1. *to saxophone*

It's al - right.___

D.S. and fade
ad lib.

2.

And in___ your___ head

I'M OUTTA LOVE

Words & Music by Anastacia, Sam Watters & Louis Biancaniello

© Copyright 2000 Breakthrough Creations/Sony/ATV Music Publishing (UK) Limited,
10 Great Marlborough Street, London W1 (42.5%)/Universal/MCA Music Limited,
77 Fulham Palace Road, London W6 (15%)/Copyright Control (42.5%).
All Rights Reserved. International Copyright Secured.

Voice: jazz organ
Rhythm: rock
Tempo: medium (♩=120)

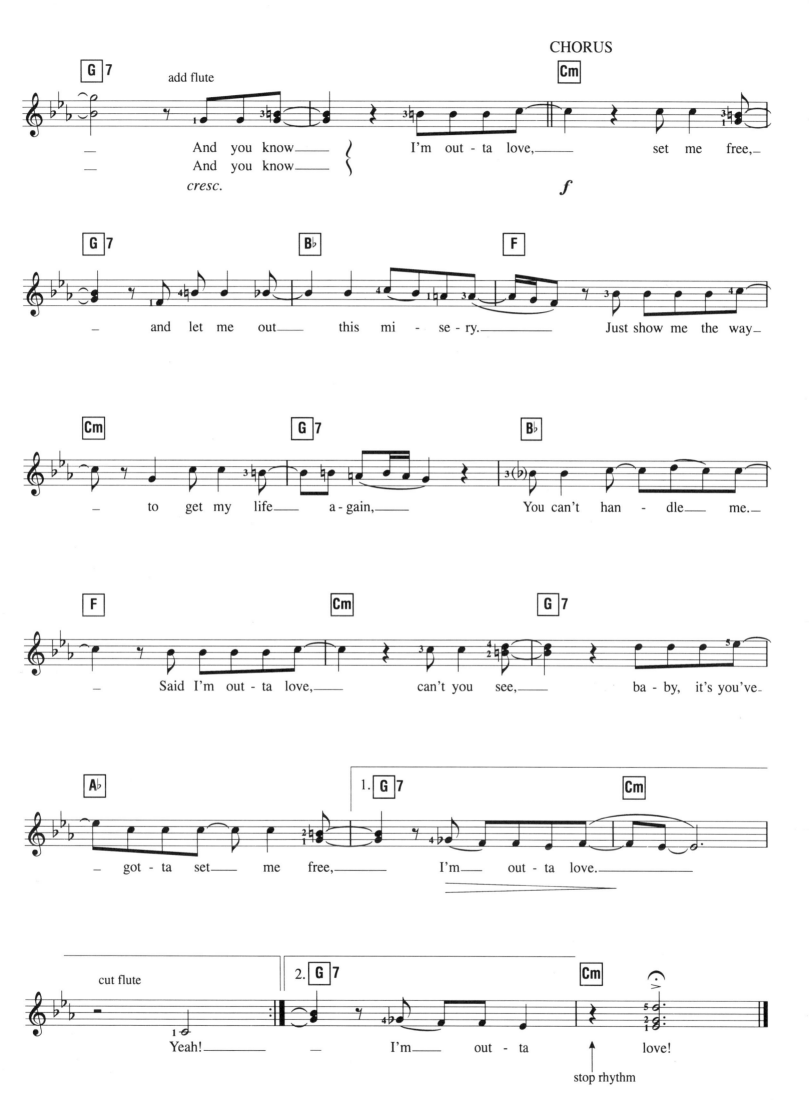

IRRESISTIBLE

**Words & Music by R.J. Lange, Andrea Corr,
Caroline Corr, Sharon Corr & Jim Corr**

© Copyright 2000 Out Of Pocket Productions Limited/Zomba Enterprises Incorporated &
Universal-Songs Of PolyGram International Incorporated/Beacon Communications Music Company, USA.
Zomba Music Publishers Limited, 165-167 High Road, London NW10 (50%)/
Universal Music Publishing Limited, 77 Fulham Palace Road, London W6 (50%).
All Rights Reserved. International Copyright Secured.

Voice: human voice

Rhythm: 8 upbeat pop

Tempo: medium (♩=126)

VERSES

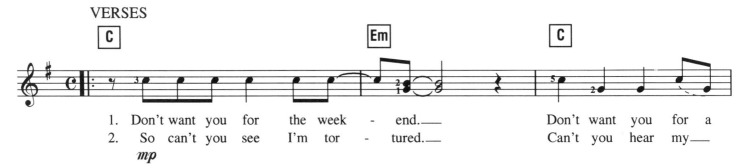

1. Don't want you for the week - end.___ Don't want you for a
2. So can't you see I'm tor - tured.___ Can't you hear my

mp

day. Don't need a love di - vi - ded.___
pain? If you just let me show___ you,___

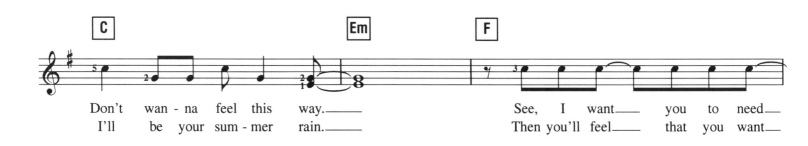

Don't wan - na feel this way.___ See, I want___ you to need___
I'll be your sum - mer rain.___ Then you'll feel___ that you want___

__ me,___ just like I need___ you.___
__ me,___ just like I want___ you.___

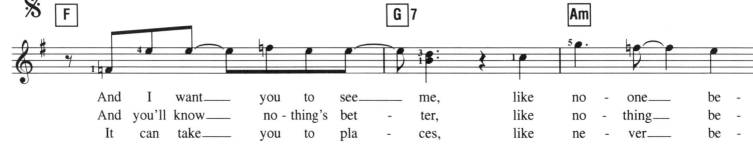

And I want___ you to see___ me, like no - one___ be -
And you'll know___ no - thing's bet - ter, like no - thing___ be -
It can take___ you to pla - ces, like ne - ver___ be -

22

STOMP

Words & Music by Mark Topham, Karl Twigg & Rita Campbell

© Copyright 2000 All Boys Music Limited, 222-224 Borough High Street, London SE1.
All Rights Reserved. International Copyright Secured.

Voice: piano
Rhythm: disco soul
Tempo: fairly fast (♩=132)

VERSES

1. Thank God for the week - end. Now is the time — for feel - in' al - right.— Come and taste the spice — of life.— To - night no - thin' mat - ters. Come and feel the groove.— Let it in - to you,— you know what you got,

2. All I need is the mu - sic to get me high.— Feel - in' so a - live. Leav - ing all my cares — be - hind.— Keep do - in' your own thing, and I'll be do - in' mine.— Danc - ing thro' the night,— this is where I feel

A7   Gm

— to do.—   Ev - 'ry   Fri - day   when   my   work   is   done,—   and,——
— al - right.—   *mp*

Dm   Gm

I   get   my   par - ty   on.———   I   call   a   few · friends   of   mine,   make   sure

Am   B♭   A7   to tenor saxophone

I'm   look - in'   fine,—   I   know   we're   gon - na   have   a   real   good   time,   yeah.
                    cresc.

CHORUS

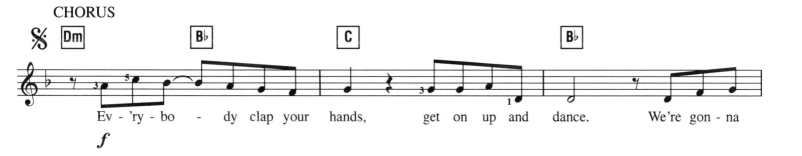

𝄋 Dm   B♭   C   B♭

Ev - 'ry - bo   dy   clap   your   hands,   get   on   up   and   dance.   We're   gon - na
  f

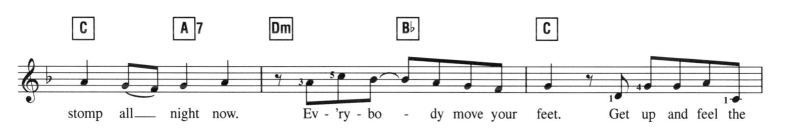

C   A7   Dm   B♭   C

stomp   all—   night   now.   Ev - 'ry - bo   dy   move   your   feet.   Get   up   and   feel   the

D.S. and fade
ad lib.

to piano

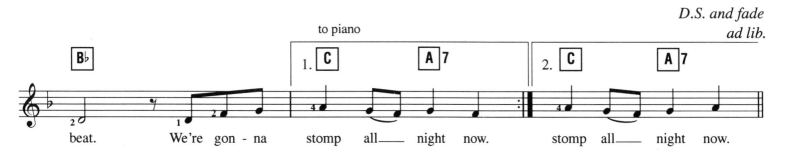

B♭   1. C   A7   2. C   A7

beat.   We're   gon - na   stomp   all—   night   now.   stomp   all—   night   now.

ROME WASN'T BUILT IN A DAY

Words & Music by Paul Godfrey, Ross Godfrey & Skye Edwards

© Copyright 2000 Chrysalis Music Limited, The Chrysalis Building, Bramley Road, London W10.
All Rights Reserved. International Copyright Secured.

Voice: jazz organ
Rhythm: rock
Tempo: medium (♩=112)

RISE

Words & Music by Bob Dylan, Gabrielle,
Ferdy Unger-Hamilton & Ollie Dagois

© Copyright 1999 Ram's Horn Music, USA (50%)/Perfect Songs Limited, The Blue Building,
42-46 St. Luke's Mews, London W11 (33.33%)/Chrysalis Music Limited, The Chrysalis Building,
Bramley Road, London W10 (16.67%).
All Rights Reserved. International Copyright Secured.

Voice: flute

Rhythm: rock pop

Tempo: slow (♩=72)

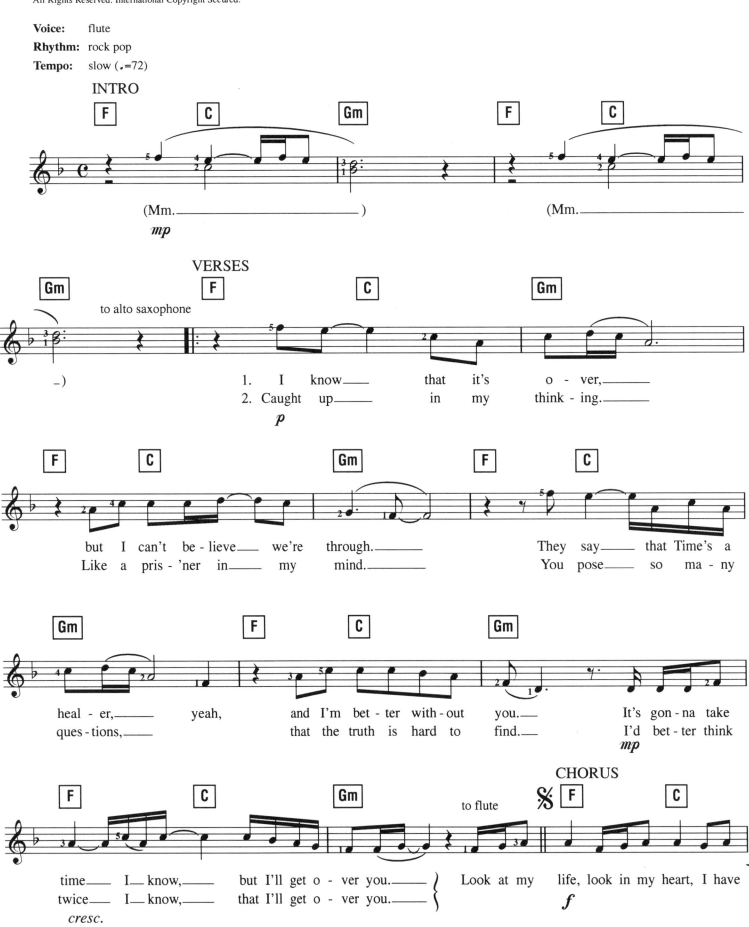

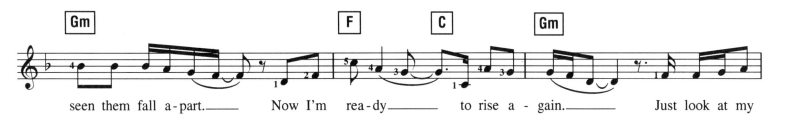

seen them fall a-part.____ Now I'm rea-dy____ to rise a - gain.____ Just look at my

hopes, look at my dreams, I'm build-ing brid-ges from_ the scenes.__ Now I'm rea-dy____ to rise a-

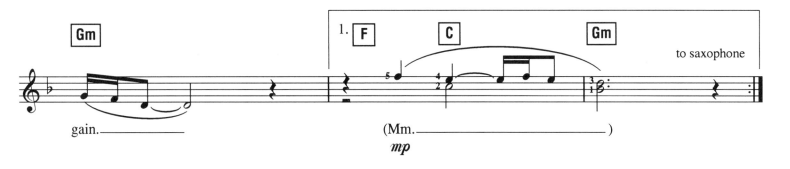

1.

to saxophone

gain.____ (Mm._____)

mp

VERSE

2.

3. Much time__ has passed be - tween us,__ mm. Do you still think of me at

p

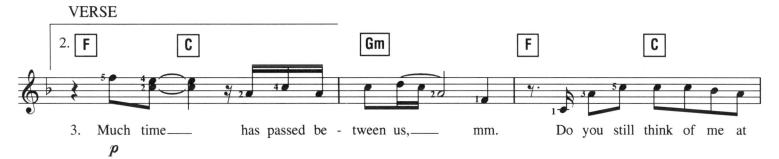

all?____ My world____ of bro-ken pro - mi - ses,____

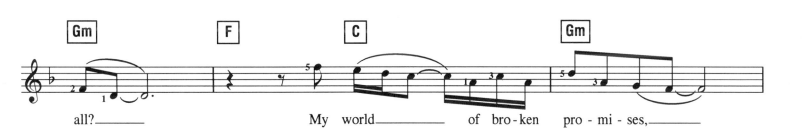

D.S. and fade
ad lib.

where you won't catch me when I fall.__ Look at my

cresc.

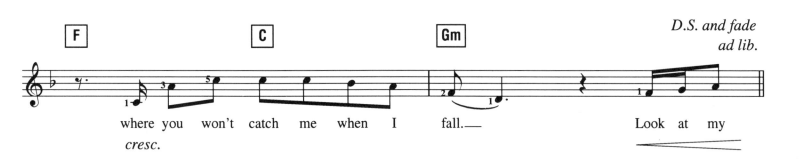

BABYLON

Words & Music by David Gray

© Copyright 1998 Chrysalis Music Limited, The Chrysalis Building, Bramley Road, London W10.
All Rights Reserved. International Copyright Secured.

Voice: 12 string guitar
Rhythm: 16 beat pop
Tempo: medium (♩=112)

VERSES

1. Fri - day night, an' I'm go - in' no - where, all the lights are chan - gin' green____ to red.____
2. Sa - tur - day, an' I'm run - nin' wild, an' all the lights are chan - gin' red____ to green.____

mp

Turn - in' o - ver T. V. sta - tions, sit - u - a - tions run - nin' thro' my
Mo - vin' through the crowds, I'm push - in', chem - i - cals are rush - in' in my

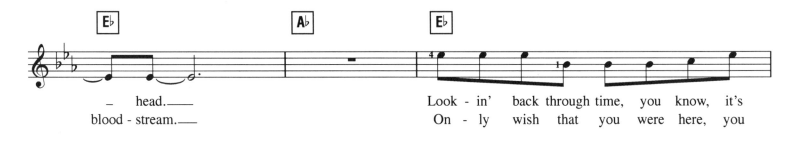

_ head.____ Look - in' back through time, you know, it's
blood - stream.____ On - ly wish that you were here, you

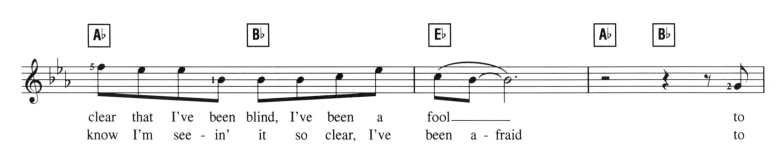

clear that I've been blind, I've been a fool____ to
know I'm see - in' it so clear, I've been a - fraid to

o - pen up my heart to all that jea - lou - sy, that bit - ter - ness, that____ ri - di - cule.
show you how I real - ly feel, ad - mit to all those bad mis - takes I've____ made.____

CHORUS

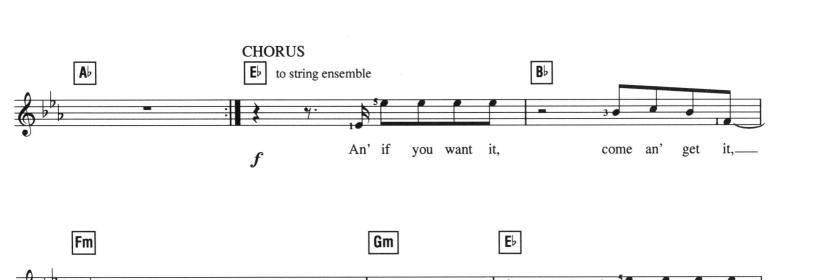

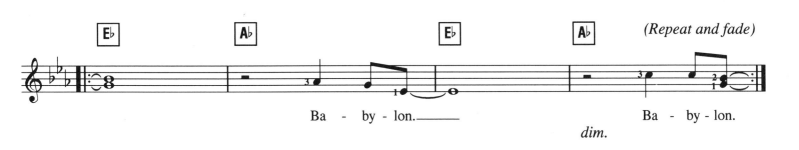

AGAINST ALL ODDS (TAKE A LOOK AT ME NOW)

Words & Music by Phil Collins

© Copyright 1984 Effectsound Limited/EMI Golden Torch Music Corporation, USA.
Hit & Run Music (Publishing) Limited, 25 Ives Street, London SW3 (75%)/
EMI Music Publishing Limited, 127 Charing Cross Road, London WC2 (25%).
All Rights Reserved. International Copyright Secured.

Voice: string ensemble
Rhythm: R & B
Tempo: slow (♩=60)

VERSES

(MALE) 1. How can I just let you walk a-way, just let you leave with-out a trace? When I

stand here ta-king ev-'ry breath with you, ooh. You're the

on - ly one who real - ly knew me at all.

(FEMALE) 2. How can you just walk a - way from me when all I can do is watch you leave? 'Cos we've
(MALE) (3.) wish I could just make you turn a - round. Turn a - round and see me cry. There's so

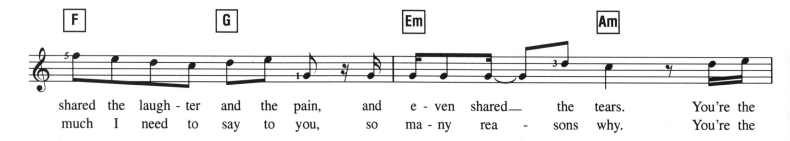

shared the laugh - ter and the pain, and e - ven shared the tears. You're the
much I need to say to you, so ma - ny rea - sons why. You're the

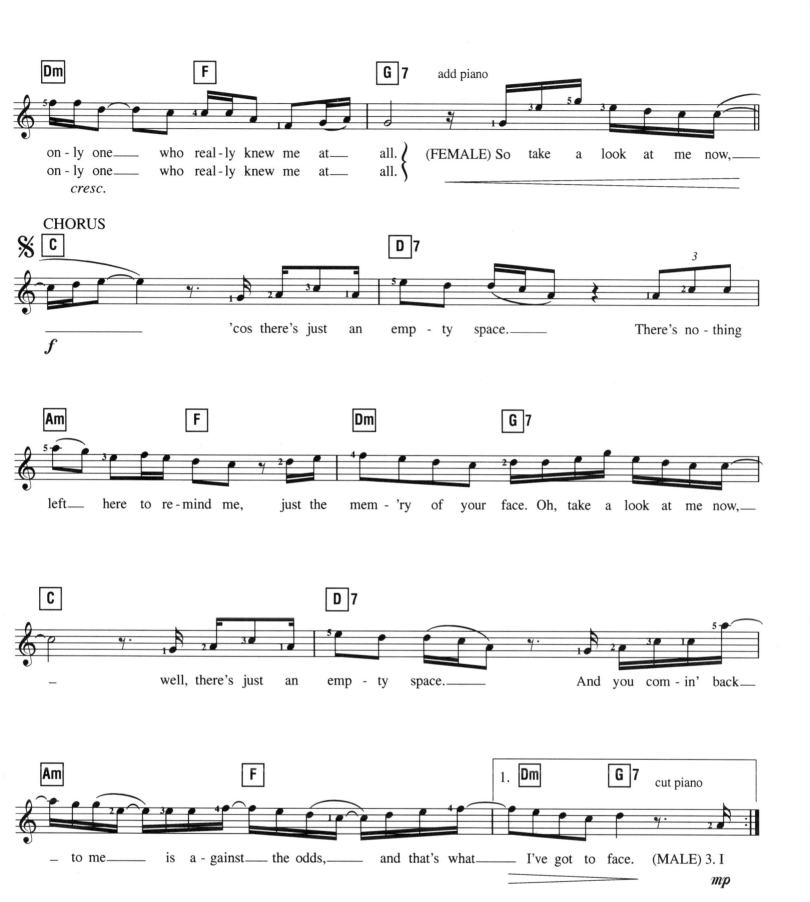

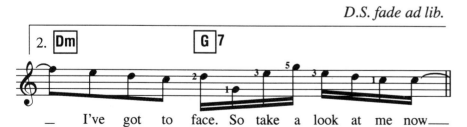

OOPS!... I DID IT AGAIN

Words & Music by Max Martin & Rami Yacoub

© Copyright 2000 Zomba Music Publishers Limited, 165-167 High Road, London NW10.
All Rights Reserved. International Copyright Secured.

Voice: synth brass
Rhythm: rock pop
Tempo: medium (♩=96)

AMERICAN PIE

Words & Music by Don McLean

© Copyright 1971 Music Corporation Of America Incorporated & Benny Bird Company Incorporated, USA.
Universal/MCA Music Limited, 77 Fulham Palace Road, London W6.
All Rights Reserved. International Copyright Secured.

Voice: flute

Rhythm: 8 beat ballad

Tempo: medium (♩=104)

INTRO

freely {♩=68 approx.}

Rhythm: off

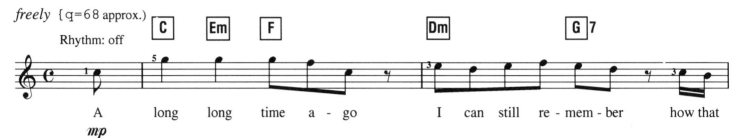

A long long time a-go I can still re-mem-ber how that

mu-sic used to make me smile. And I knew that if I had my chance, I could make those peo-ple dance, and

VERSES
(rhythm starts)

Synchro: on

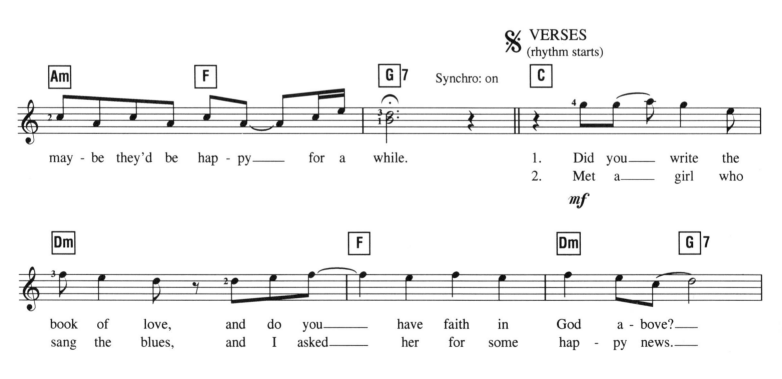

may-be they'd be hap-py——— for a while.

1. Did you——— write the
2. Met a——— girl who

book of love, and do you——— have faith in God a-bove?———
sang the blues, and I asked——— her for some hap-py news.———

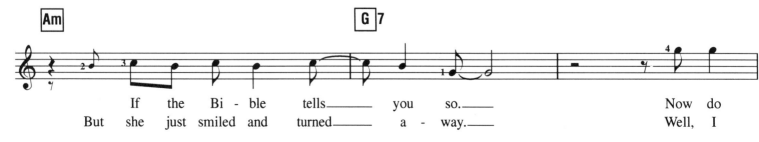

If the Bi-ble tells——— you so.———
But she just smiled and turned——— a-way.———

Now do
Well, I

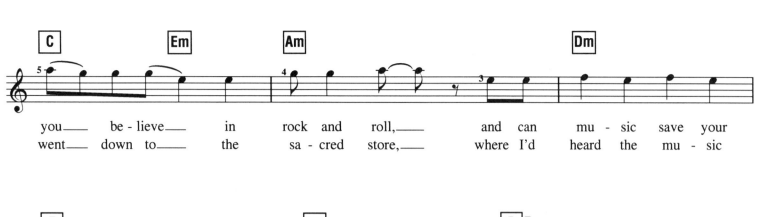

you___ be - lieve___ in rock and roll,___ and can mu - sic save your
went___ down to___ the sa - cred store,___ where I'd heard the mu - sic

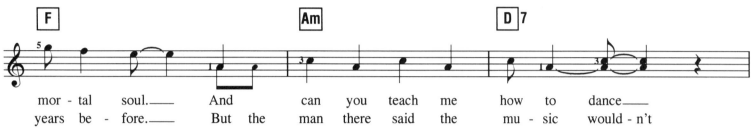

mor - tal soul.___ And can you teach me how to dance___
years be - fore.___ But the man there said the mu - sic would - n't

to clarinet

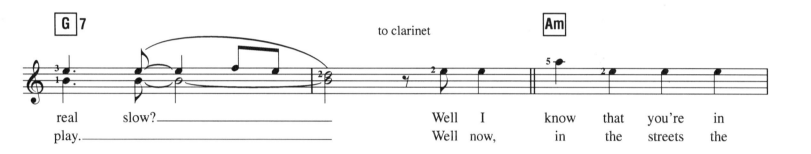

real slow?___ Well I know that you're in
play.___ Well now, in the streets the

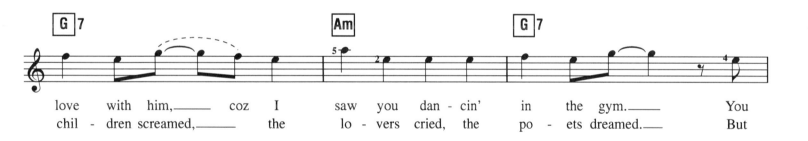

love with him,___ coz I saw you dan - cin' in the gym.___ You
chil - dren screamed,___ the lo - vers cried, the po - ets dreamed.___ But

both kicked off your shoes.___ Man, I dig those rhy - thm and blues.___
not a word was spo - ken the church bells all were bro - ken.___

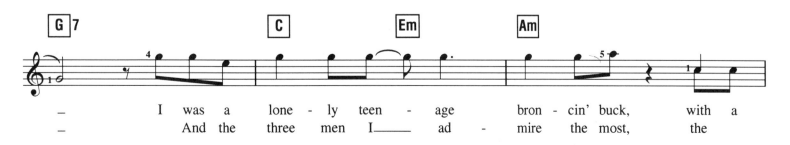

_ I was a lone - ly teen - age bron - cin' buck, with a
_ And the three men I___ ad - mire the most, the

pink car - na - tion and a pick - up truck.___ But I knew that I was out___
Fath - er, Son and the___ Ho - ly Ghost,___ they caught the last train for___

_ of luck___ the day___ the mu - sic died.
_ the coast,___ the day___ the mu - sic died.___

add piano and strings

CHORUS

_
_ I start - ed sing - ing: bye___ bye, Miss A -
We start - ed sing - ing: *f*

me - ri - can Pie.___ Drove my Che - vy to the lev - ee, but the lev - ee was dry.___ Them

good ole___ boys___ were drink - in' whis - ky and rye,___ sing - in' "This will be the day that I

D.S. (fade on CHORUS)

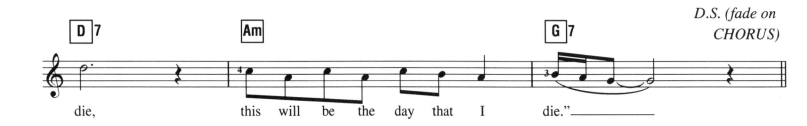

die, this will be the day that I die."___

CHORD CHARTS (For Left Hand)

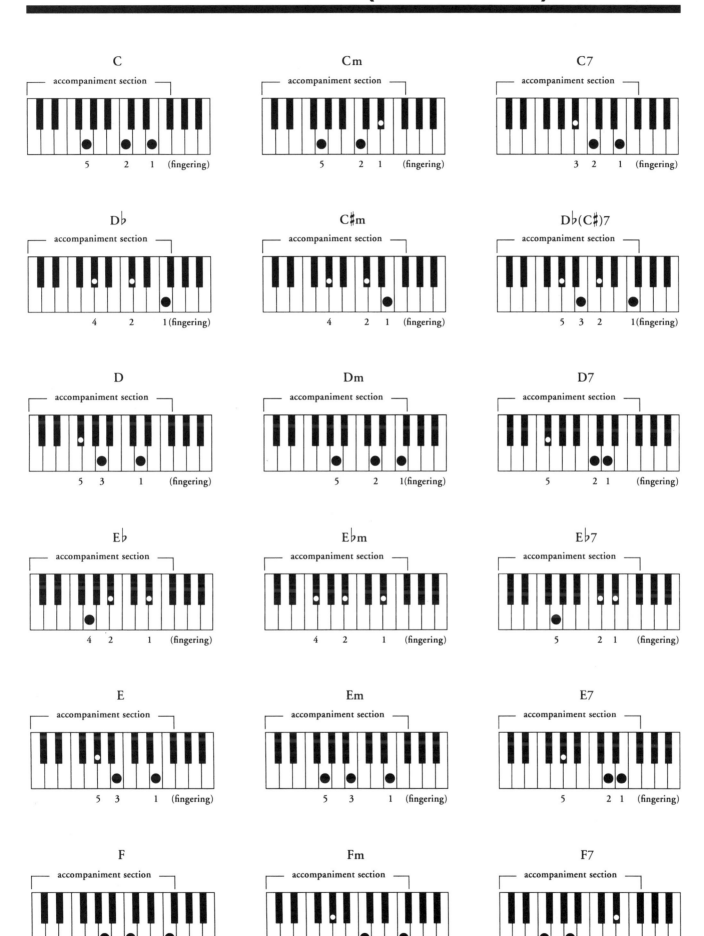

CHORD CHARTS (For Left Hand)

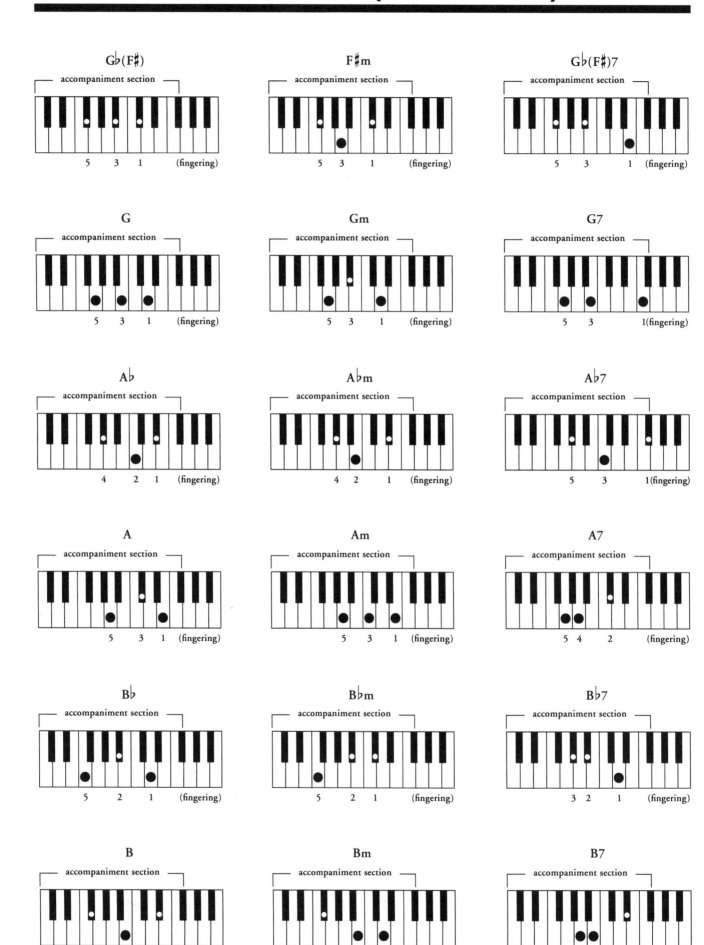